C000196620

Flute
Grade 7

Pieces
for Trinity College London exams

2017-2020

Published by
Trinity College London Press Ltd
trinitycollege.com

Registered in England
Company no. 09726123

Printed in England by Caligraving Ltd

Adagio and Allegro

1st and 2nd movements from *Sonata no. 4 in D major*

C P E Bach
(1714-1788)

4

8

Flute
Grade 7

Pieces
for Trinity College London exams

2017-2020

Published by
Trinity College London Press Ltd
trinitycollege.com

Registered in England
Company no. 09726123

TCL 015563
ISBN 978-0-85736-511-8

Contents

Adagio and Allegro

1st and 2nd movements from *Sonata no. 4 in D major*

C P E Bach
(1714–1788)

Allegro non molto

1st movement from *Concerto in G*

Christoph Willibald Gluck
(1714-1787)

* Start here for exam performance

* Cadenza to be played in exam

Allegro ritmico

1st movement from *Sonatina*, op. 98

William Mathias
(1934-1992)

[Blank page to facilitate page turns]

Sonata no. 7 in F

Giuseppe Rabboni
(1800-1856)

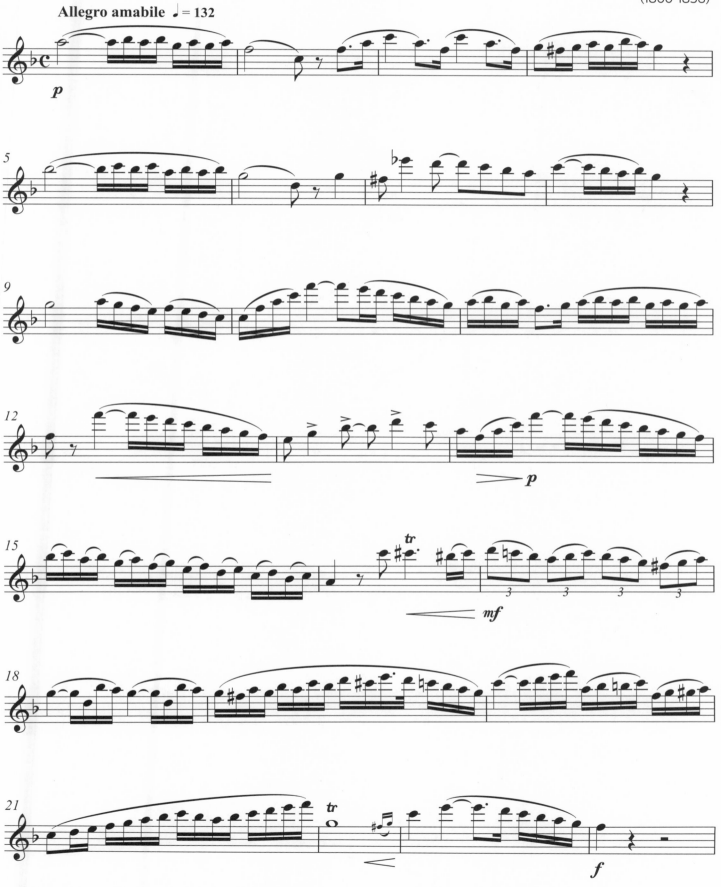

Krishna and Mr. de la Péjaudie

from *Joueurs de Flûte*, op. 27

Albert Roussel
(1869–1937)

Krishna

Mr. de la Péjaudie

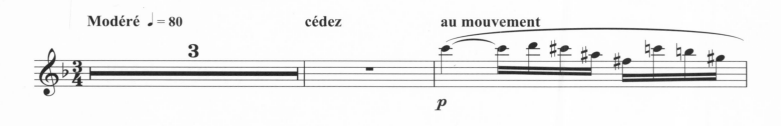

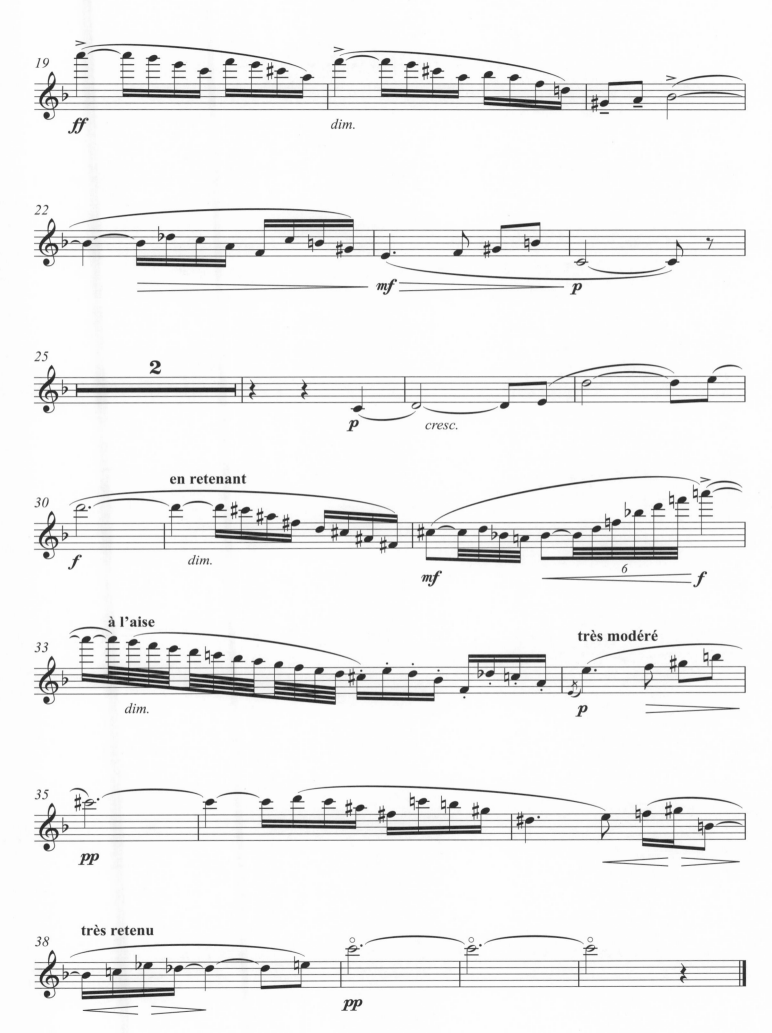

Three Minute Sonata

Gary Schocker
(b. 1959)

*To achieve this effect, finger the F and add both R.H. trill keys, blowing gently to split the airstream.

Poco lento and Allegro con grazia

1st movement from *Sonatina for Solo Flute*

Richard Rodney Bennett
(1936-2012)

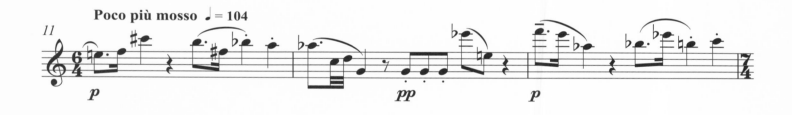

Allegro moderato

1st movement from *Capriccio-Sonata* in A major

Anton Stamitz
(1750-1789/1809)

25

Tango Etude no. 5

Astor Piazzolla
(1921–1992)

Allegro non molto

1st movement from *Concerto in G*

Christoph Willibald Gluck
(1714-1787)

* Start here for exam performance

14

* Cadenza to be played in exam

Allegro ritmico

1st movement from *Sonatina*, op. 98

William Mathias
(1934–1992)

Sonata no. 7 in F

Giuseppe Rabboni
(1800-1856)

Flute part edited by Paul Edmund-Davies, Piano accompaniment composed by Roger Vignoles

Krishna and Mr. de la Péjaudie

from *Joueurs de Flûte*, op. 27

Albert Roussel
(1869–1937)

Krishna

Mr. de la Péjaudie

Three Minute Sonata

I.

Gary Schocker
(b. 1959)

*To achieve this effect, finger the F and add both R.H. trill keys, blowing gently to split the airstream.